# Reading Together

# Goldilocks
## and the Three Bears

Phonics Consultant: Susan Purcell

Illustrator: Francesca Assirelli

Concept: Fran Bromage

ng   ng

air

y   igh

Miles Kelly

Emphasize the b sound (as in big) as you read aloud

Once upon a time, there were three bears, who lived in a big house by a big wood.

**Say** the names as you spot each bear.

 **Stick on** the bear stickers.

Daddy Bear

Mummy Bear

Baby Bear

There was Daddy Bear,
Mummy Bear and little
Baby Bear.

What a good try! Put a gold star here. Well done!

**Sound out** the things in the picture beginning with **b** as you find them.

bear     ball     butterfly
bush     basket

Focus on
the o sound
(as in hot)

Every day, the bears liked to eat a lot of porridge for breakfast. One morning, it was too hot to eat.

**Sound out** these words with the o sound.

top    cot    fox    nod

job    dog    spot    clock

4

We will walk this way.

So the three bears left the house and went for a walk in the wood.

Use your stickers to **spell** some words beginning with **w**.

web    won    wet    wig

Among the trees, a girl called Goldilocks was growing worried.

She had drifted off a green, grassy trail and was trying to find her way home.

**Say** the names of the things in the picture, as you spot them.

branch   dress   grass   trunk

6

Goldilocks saw a **br**ick house with a **br**own door.

Inside, she could see the bears' **br**eakfast. As she was **gr**owing hungry and needed a **dr**ink, she went inside.

Use your stickers to **spell** some words beginning with **br**, **dr**, **gr** and **tr**.

 **ush**    **op**   **gr**ip    **ack**

Highlight
the oa sound
(as in toast)

The table was loaded with food. There were plates of toast and three bowls of oat porridge too.

The porridge in the big red bowl was much too hot.

The porridge in the medium purple bowl was too lumpy.

**Sound out** these words, which all have the **oa** sound.

show    grow    hole    mole

coat    boat    toe

But the porridge in the small blue bowl was just right, so Goldilocks ate it all!

Say the words as you spot each bowl.

Stick on the bowl stickers.

big red bowl

medium purple bowl

small blue bowl

9

Next, Goldilocks went to explore. She saw three chairs – a big wooden chair, a medium purple chair and a small stripy chair.

**Say** the words as you spot each chair.

**Stick on** the chair stickers.

big chair

medium chair

small chair

When she tried the big chair it was much too hard.

The medium chair was much too soft, but the small chair was just right.

Sound out these words, which all have the ch sound.

chin    chop    chart    chick

rich    beach    church

Sound out the
sh sound (as in
crash)

Goldilocks sat on the
little chair. In a flash,
the chair broke, and
Goldilocks fell on the
floor with a crash.

**Stick on**
some words
that rhyme
with fla**sh**.

**Sound out** these words, which all end with the **sh** sound.

cash     push     fish     dash

posh     rush     wish

12

Goldilocks didn't **stop**.
She **stood** up quickly, and
**stamped** up the **stairs**.

Emphasize the st blend, as you read

Use your stickers to **spell** some words beginning with **st**.

**st**ick    **st**ep    **st**ay    **st**uck

**Emphasize the e sound (as in bed)**

When Goldilocks got to the bedroom, she saw three beds. Feeling tired, she headed towards the big bed, but it was very hard.

The medium bed was very soft, but the small bed was just right.

Use your arrow stickers to **point** to some things that are red.

**Sound out** these words with the **e** sound.

peg   shed   hen   egg

deaf   tread   bread   sweat

14

**Say** the words as you spot things with the **e** sound.

**Stick on** their stickers.

teddy

head

bed

15

Highlight the ng sound (as in walking)

Soon, the three bears arrived home. Walking had been hard work, so they were looking forward to eating a big breakfast.

Use your stickers to **spell** some words with the **ng** ending.

feeling     reading
singing     talking

16

"Someone's been eating my porridge," said Daddy Bear, looking cross.

"Someone's been eating my porridge," said Mummy Bear, looking worried.

"Someone's been eating my porridge," said Baby Bear, looking sad. "And they've eaten it all up!"

Use a sticker to **complete** the sentence with the **ng** sound.

"Someone's been eating my porridge," said Baby Bear.

17

Next, the three bears saw their three chairs.

"Someone's been sitting in my chair," said Daddy Bear.

"Someone's been sitting in my chair," said Mummy Bear.

"Someone's been sitting in my chair," said Baby Bear. "And they've broken it into bits!"

Use your stickers to **spell** some words that end in the **air** sound.

hair      stair      pair      fair

18

Then the three bears went upstairs.

"Someone's been sleeping in my bed," said Daddy Bear.

"Someone's been sleeping in my bed," said Mummy Bear.

**Sound out** these words with the **air** sound.

bear     spare     dare     care

square     where     there

"Someone's been sleeping in my bed," said Baby Bear. "And they're still lying there!"

When Goldilocks saw the bears, she got quit**e** a fr**igh**t, and gave a cry!

**Sound out** these words with the **ie** sound.

pie    tie    sigh    high

try    fry    like    bike    eye

Use your stickers to **spell** these words, which all use the **ie** sound.

sky  spy  dry
night  right

Emphasize the r sound (as in ran)

Goldilocks **raced** **right** out of the house. She **ran** away **really** fast and the three bears never saw her again.

Use your stickers to **spell** some words beginning with r.

rat     rain     rug     ring     red

22

Ask your child to **retell** the story using these key sounds and story images.

hot

walk

breakfast

bowl

chair

bed

looking

cry

ran

Use your stickers to **add** a word that matches
the red highlighted **sounds** on each line.

basket    bush    trail    [ ball ]

tie

drink    drifted    dress

grip    growing    green

trunk    trees    track

step

grass

fish    rush    smash

stick    stood    walking    stop

feeling    looking    eating    stair

bear    hair    care    crash

high    bike    cry

24    You've had fun with phonics! Well done.